MERRY CHRISTMAS

A Book of Carols for Piano Solo

by Jane Smisor Bastien

ISBN 0-8497-6007-0

GENERAL WORDS & MUSIC CO., Publisher

O Come, All Ye Faithful

John Reading

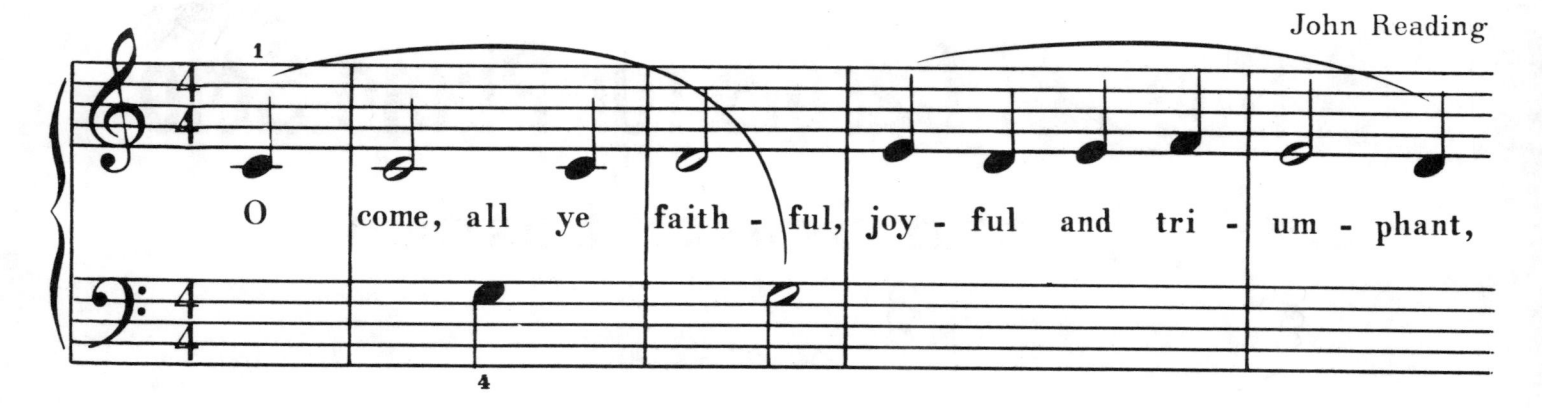

O come, all ye faith-ful, joy-ful and tri - um - phant,

Hark! The Herald Angels Sing

Felix Mendelssohn

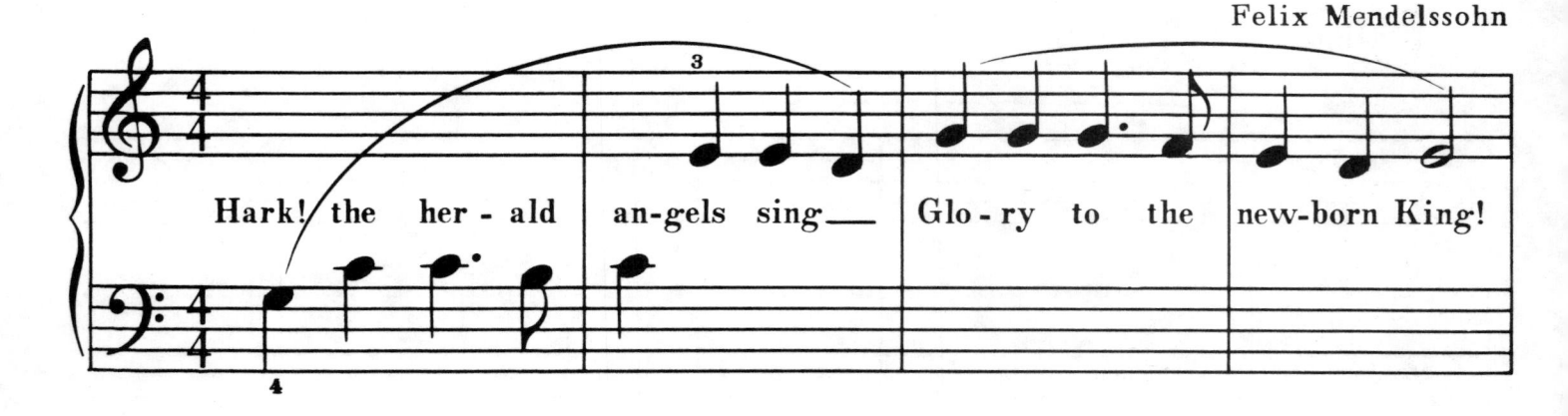

Hark! the her-ald an-gels sing— Glo-ry to the new-born King!

Peace on earth and mer-cy mild,— God and sin-ners rec-on-ciled.

Joy-ful, all ye na-tions, rise,— Join the tri-umph of the skies;—

With an-gel-ic host pro-claim, Christ is— born in Beth-le-hem!

Hark! the her-ald an-gels sing, Glo-ry to the new-born King!

Away In A Manger

German Carol

A - way   in   a   man - ger, no   crib   for   a   bed,

The   lit - tle Lord   Je - sus   lay down   His   sweet   head;

The   stars   in   the   heav - ens looked down where   He   lay,

The   lit — tle   Lord

Je - sus a-sleep in the   hay.

Deck The Halls

Old Welsh Air

Deck the halls with boughs of hol - ly, Fa - la - la - la - la - la - la - la - la!

'Tis the sea - son to be jol - ly, Fa - la - la - la - la - la - la - la - la!

Don we now our gay ap - par - el, Fa - la - la - la - la - la - la - la - la!

Troll the an - cient Yule - tide car - ol, Fa - la - la - la - la - la - la - la - la!

The First Noel

French Carol

The first ___ No - el the an - gels did say

O Little Town of Bethlehem

Lewis H. Redner

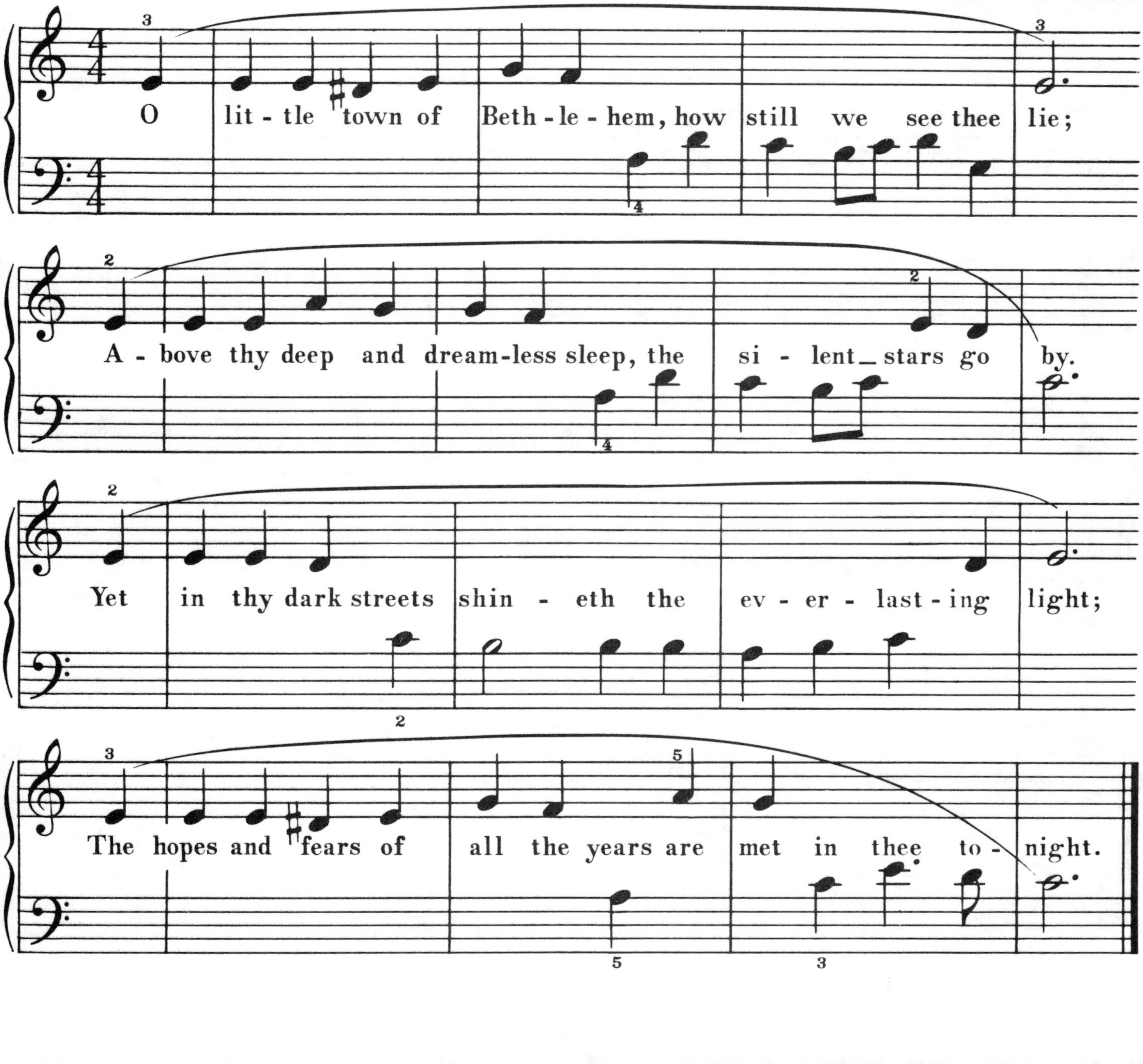

O lit - tle town of Beth - le - hem, how still we see thee lie;

A - bove thy deep and dream-less sleep, the si - lent stars go by.

Yet in thy dark streets shin - eth the ev - er - last - ing light;

The hopes and fears of all the years are met in thee to - night.

Silent Night

Franz Gruber

Si - lent night, Ho - ly night, All is calm,

All is bright, 'Round yon vir - gin Moth - er and Child,

Ho - ly In - fant so ten - der and mild, Sleep in heav - en - ly

peace, ____ Sleep ___ in heav - en - ly peace.

Jolly Old Saint Nicholas

Traditional

Jol - ly old Saint Nich - o - las, Lean your ear this way,

Don't you tell a sin - gle soul, What I'm going to say;

Christ - mas Eve is com - ing soon, Now you dear old man,

Whis - per what you'll bring to me, Tell me if you can.

Jingle Bells

J. Pierpont

Oh, what fun it is to ride in a one-horse o-pen sleigh!

Jin-gle bells, Jin-gle bells, Jin-gle all the way!

Oh, what fun it is to ride in a one-horse o-pen sleigh!

Good King Wenceslas

English Carol

Good King Wen - ces - las looked out, On the feast of Ste - phen,

When the snow lay round a - bout, Deep and crisp and e - ven.

Bright-ly shone the moon that night, Tho' the frost was cru - el,

When a poor man came in sight, Gath-'ring win - ter fu - el.